D0318924

We Just Had a Baby

written by Stephen Krensky

illustrated by Amélie Graux

First published in 2016 by Curious Fox,
an imprint of Capstone Global Library Limited
264 Banbury Road, Oxford OX2 7DY
Registered company number: 6695582

www.curious-fox.com

Text copyright © Stephen Krensky 2016
Illustrations copyright © Curious Fox 2016

The author's moral rights are hereby asserted.
Illustrations by Amélie Graux

ISBN 978 1 78202 342 5

19 18 17 16 15
10 9 8 7 6 5 4 3 2 1

A CIP catalogue for this book is available from the British Library.

Printed and bound in China.

For Andrew and Nicole,
who both came first.
—S.K.

Pour Rachid, mon amour,
pour nos futurs petits choux.
—Amélie

We just had a baby.
It wasn't my idea.

She took a while to get here.
We waited and waited.

It seemed to
take forever.

And after all that waiting,
there she was.

I thought she
would be bigger.

The baby blinks and wiggles.
Everyone thinks
this is amazing.

When I blink and wiggle,
nobody even notices.

We both have ten fingers
and ten toes. I counted
to make sure.

Mine are bigger.

The baby wears
a nappy. She doesn't
know what else to do.

I am way ahead of her.

The baby grabs my finger.
She holds on tight.

I guess she likes me.

The baby just drinks milk.
No pizza. No ice cream.

Too bad for baby!

The baby takes
a bath every day.
She is learning
how to splash.

I'm a good teacher.

The baby makes noises.
She giggles and coos
and burps.

And she cries. A lot.
That's what she
does best.

Now the baby rolls over.
But she doesn't roll back —
even after I showed her how!

The baby likes to play peek-a-boo.
But I have to do all the work.

When I smile
at the baby, the
baby smiles back.

When I frown
at the baby, the
baby looks scared.

I try to smile most of the time.

I'm glad the baby
keeps trying new things.
I hope she grows up soon.

I have BIG plans
for us!